Extreme Race

by

Jane A. C. West

Illustrated by Dylan Gibson

To Wanda, who ran the
Marathon des Sables and has triumphed
over illness and injury.

With special thanks to:

Josh Allinson
Rebecca Brant
Jake Cain
Yasmin Ewers
Elliot Fane
Harry Leighfield
William Mullins
Louise Norris
Sarah Norris
Kirstie Tracey

First published in 2010 in Great Britain by
Barrington Stoke Ltd
18 Walker St, Edinburgh, EH3 7LP

www.barringtonstoke.co.uk

ISBN: 978-1-84299-833-5

Printed in Great Britain by Bell & Bain Ltd

Contents

WITHDRAWN FROM STOCK

Chapter 1
School's Out

"No more school, bro!" said Mark. "That's it for ever."

He had a huge smile on his face.

"Yes!" said Ben. "Soon I'll have a job. And you'll be bumming around at Uni."

Mark's smile faded. "I wish you were going to Uni, too. It won't be the same without you – you'll leave a gap in our team."

Ben gave a sigh. "I know. But I can't leave Belle by herself at home. Mum and Dad are great, but she'd be so fed up if I went away. You know she can't get out much."

Belle was Ben's twin sister and she was very ill. Most of the time she was too sick to leave her room. Sometimes she went to stay at a care home, the nearby hospice, so nurses could look after her and Mum and Dad could have a rest. She had cystic fibrosis – her lungs didn't work properly – and she was hoping for a transplant operation to get new ones. She had been waiting a long time.

Mark stared at the ground. "I wish I could help Belle."

"I know," said Ben. "But no one can help. Not even me. Not really."

They didn't say any more about it. Sometimes there are no words to say.

"I've got an idea," said Mark suddenly. "I still think we should do something cool. Leaving school is a big deal."

"Maybe," said Ben. "But I don't feel much like having a party."

"No, not a party," said Mark. "Something that really means a lot. Something to help Belle."

"You're thinking," said Ben. "I can hear your brain clanking."

"Yeah, well, I've got a crazy idea," said Mark. "There was a programme on TV about long distance runs. These people were running across the Sahara desert in Africa – they call it an *extreme* marathon race. Some of them raised lots of money for charity."

Ben stared at him. "You think we could ..."

"Yes!" said Mark. "We could do the run and raise money for Belle's hospice. What do you think?"

"What do I think? I think you're right – but you're crazy too. You get out of breath running for the bus. How are you going to run for days in the Sahara desert?"

"Well, we'd have to start training at once," said Mark. "But we could do it. You used to run a lot when you were younger."

"That's different. I mean – a marathon! That's just over 26 miles," said Ben.

"Er ... well ... this race in the desert is 151 miles," said Mark. "But you get six days to do it."

"You're kidding!"

"Nope. Come on," said Mark. "It will be amazing."

Ben slowly began to smile. It was a wild idea – but why not? It would be fun to train with Mark. Even better, they could raise money for Belle's hospice. Maybe they could help her after all. And she would know that they cared about her.

"Let's do it!" said Ben.

Chapter 2
Training

Ben couldn't wait to tell Belle about their plan.

"You guys are crazy, but I love you," she said.

The idea was great but now it was very real. "This training is harder than I thought," gasped Mark.

He sat on the ground.

Ben jogged slowly on the spot. He was enjoying the training. They had been working at it for six weeks. Ben was in

better shape than Mark.

"We should start training with back-packs soon," said Ben. "We're going to have to carry eight kg in the desert. We have to take food and water and a sleeping bag and lots of other things."

"Give me a break, bro," said Mark. "You're getting a bit too keen. This is meant to be fun. Remember?"

Ben frowned. Yes, this marathon in the sun was meant to be fun. But if they didn't train, they would never finish the race. Then there would be no money to give to Belle's hospice.

Ben said nothing. He could see Mark was in no mood to hear the truth.

He tried to sound up-beat.

"The fund raising is going well. That big sports store in town is going to sponsor us."

"That's great news," said Mark. "That makes nearly £7,000 already."

Ben smiled. "OK. Rest break over. Let's get going."

The next day Ben went to the gym. Running was good training, but they needed to pump some iron, too. Ben waited for

Mark. After half an hour, he decided Mark wasn't coming.

"It's his deal," he said to himself. "If he doesn't train, he won't finish the race."

But Ben was worried. It wasn't going to be easy. This desert marathon was no picnic. It was one of the hardest races in the world. It was extreme.

At home, Ben looked at the list of stuff
they needed. It was a long list.

Back-pack

A light sleeping bag

Torch

Compass

Lighter

Mirror

First aid kit

Spare clothes

Food (and a gas
burner to cook it)

Spork

Sun block

Sunglasses and hat

Gaiters

"Why do I need a mirror?" he said to
himself. "There are no showers. I won't
wash for a week. What are 'gaiters'?
What's a 'spork'? It sounds like something
from *Star Trek*."

He read the info again. The mirror wasn't so he could check his hair gel – it was to signal for help. In the desert, people could see the flash of sun on glass for miles. The gaiters were pieces of rubber to put over your trainers – they kept the sand out of your socks.

"Good idea," said Ben to himself. "If you have sand in your socks it means you'll get bad blisters."

The 'spork' was a cross between a spoon and a fork. Very useful when every little extra mattered – and everything had to be carried on your back.

"There's something missing from that list," he said. "Bog paper. I'll put that at the top."

Chapter 3
Africa

Four months later they were in Africa.

Belle, sitting in her wheel-chair, had seen them off at the airport.

It was hot. Oh, boy, it was hot!

In Britain it was winter, cold and grey.
In Africa, the light bounced off the ground.
Even the air smelled hot – like burnt paper.
Ben put on his sun-glasses.

Mark smiled. "I'll get a great tan."

They were excited. Lots of other people on the plane were doing the marathon. They talked about their training. Most of them had trained for two years. Ben felt nervous. Mark and he had only trained for six months.

"Don't worry, son."

The man who spoke to him was thin but fit. He looked older than Ben's grandad. "You'll be OK if you've done your training. My tip is don't carry too much food. Digesting your food uses up energy – keep your energy for running."

"Thanks!" said Ben. "I'll remember that."

The man shook hands with him.

"See you at the finish, son."

Everyone seemed very friendly. Most people were there just for the challenge – to test themselves, not to try and win the marathon. The record was 151 miles in 19 hours. That was an average speed of eight mph. Ben could run that for two or three miles – but not for 151 miles – and not in this heat. It was already over 35°C and it was still morning.

More than 800 people were running the race.

It was the day before the race started. The tents were set up in a U-shape near the start. Each runner was given a number and told which tent to share.

Ben and Mark were sharing with six big, tough soldiers who told jokes. They were sure that they would finish the race with fast times.

"It's all in the mind, mate," said one soldier to Ben and Mark. "Training isn't enough – you've got to tell your brain you'll do it. That's the secret."

"Leave off," said another. "Hours training in the gym are the real secret. You've got to put in the work."

"No," said another. "Work in the gym won't get you ready for a run like this. You've got to train outside. We'll be running on sand dunes and rocky ground. That's nothing like running on a machine in the gym."

"Don't mind them, kid," said the one who seemed like the boss. "Just relax and enjoy it. It's meant to be fun!"

Mark, Ben and the soldiers talked late into the night. The stars were bright and the air was cool. They could see the flicker of small fires across the desert. There were no toilets, so people crept into the sand dunes and did what they had to do. The specks of fire were people burning their toilet paper. From a distance, it looked pretty.

Ben was wide awake. He could hear
Mark and the soldiers snoring. He could
hear the blood pounding in his head and his
heart was racing. He tried to focus on
breathing slowly. At last he felt calmer. He
fell asleep with the silent desert all around
him.

Chapter 4
Sun Run

The marathon was about to start. Ben and Mark took their places in the line up. The runners were given maps in case they got lost. The best runners went first. The rest were sent off in large groups. Each person would be timed. Most people just wanted to finish.

"Who dares, wins!" said Mark.

Ben nodded. "Let's do it for Belle."

The first few miles were easy. Then the path got steeper and the ground was rocky. Ben had to focus on not falling. The day got hotter. Everyone was soaked in sweat.

Some looked as if they had sunburn already.

Ben's feet were sore. It was hard

running on small stones. His mouth was dry

and full of sand – he couldn't even spit.

Every few miles there were people waiting to give the runners water.

"Bro, this is hard work!" gasped Mark. "I'd kill for an ice cream."

Ben smiled. "Dream on. It's going to be dry food tonight, and a tent full of sweaty soldiers."

"Got any good news?" said Mark with a groan.

Ben could see that Mark was getting tired. They ran side by side.

"We're almost there now. Three more miles and we've done it for today," said Ben.

They were overtaken by a girl. She had long brown hair and long brown legs.

"No worries, bro," said Mark. "I never felt better."

It was an amazing feeling when they finished the first day. They'd run 12 miles. It had been an easy day to break them in. The next day they had to do 17 miles. The race got harder – and longer – each day.

Mark was on top form. He spent the evening going from tent to tent, telling jokes, and looking for the girl with the long brown legs.

Ben lay back in his sleeping bag, staring at the stars. He was soon fast asleep.

The next day Ben was awake early. He had breakfast with the soldiers. Mark was still rolled up in his sleeping bag. Ben did a warm-up to stretch his legs. He was pleased that he didn't have too many sore bits. Lots of runners had sore shoulders from their back-packs. Ben was pleased that his back-pack was one of the lightest.

Mark groaned. Ben could see he was stiff and sore all over.

"How many miles today?" Mark asked

"Just 17," Ben told him. "You've run more than that back home. Tomorrow it's 19. The hardest day is the day after that – 40 miles. But I know we can do it."

Mark looked worried, but said, "A walk in the park, bro."

They started off slowly. Soon Mark's stiff muscles got looser and they ran faster. They made good time. Not as fast as the leaders, but pretty good.

The next day was harder. The sand dunes were high. It was hard work running up them and sliding down the other side.

Lots of people slipped and twisted their ankles.

Everyone was quiet that night in the camp. They all knew that the next day would be very hard indeed – 40 miles across the desert.

Mark's feet had a few blisters. Some people had such bad blisters that the skin peeled off in sheets. By now 50 people had dropped out of the race. Some had twisted ankles, some had sunburn – two were in hospital with sun stroke.

Ben and Mark were doing well. But the desert wasn't finished with them yet.

Chapter 5
Sand-storm

Ben watched as Mark crawled out of his sleeping bag. He groaned as he pulled his trainers on over his blisters. He told fewer jokes now. But his set face showed how much he wanted to finish the marathon.

"Let's do it, bro," he said.

They had run ten miles when the sky turned black.

"I think it's going to rain," said Mark.

"No way," said Ben. "We're in a desert and it's 40°C. It must be a sand-storm."

"Oh, hell! You're right. We'd better try and get to the next check-point."

"No, man," said Ben. "They told us to stay still if there's a sand-storm, or we could get lost."

"Forget that," said Mark. "I don't want to get caught in a sand-storm. Come on. We can make it if we go fast."

Ben didn't want to carry on. But he didn't want to stay by himself either.

The wind blew hard. Ben's eyes were gritty with sand and it was hard to breathe.

"We've got to stop, Mark!" he shouted into the wind. "We're not going to make it to the next check-point."

"OK. You were right. Let's wait over there."

Mark ran towards a sand dune. He hoped it would give them shelter from the sand-storm.

"Oh, no!" he yelled. "My sleeping bag has blown away!"

They watched as Mark's sleeping bag slid down the dune and out of sight.

"Leave it!" shouted Ben.

Mark couldn't hear him. He ran down the dune, chasing his sleeping bag.

Ben tried to follow.

"Mark!" he yelled. "Mark!"

He was blinded by sand. He could hardly stand and he couldn't see Mark at all.

Ben kneeled down and waited for the
sand-storm to finish. He tried not to panic.
"He'll be OK," he said to himself. "Mark is fit
and strong. He'll be OK. Please, God!"

The storm raged for an hour. It stopped as suddenly as it had started. The sky was clear and blue again.

"Mark! Mark! Where are you?" Ben shouted loudly. There was no answer.

"Now what do I do?" he said to himself. "Do I look for Mark, or do I go for help?" He felt sick with fear.

He shouted again. Silence.

He ran to the next dune. He saw a piece of cloth sticking out of the sand. His heart thudded in his chest.

The cloth was Mark's sleeping bag. Mark was lying next to it, buried by the sand.

"Mark! Mark! I've got you! You'll be all right!"

Ben pulled Mark out of the sand. Mark's eyes were closed.

"Come on! Don't die on me now. Come on!" he yelled.

Mark's eyes opened slowly.

"Don't worry, bro. I'm not going anywhere."

Ben laughed with relief.

"I lost my water," said Mark. "Pretty stupid, aren't I?"

"Yeah, you are. Stupid but alive!"

Ben gave him some water.

"I've twisted my ankle," said Mark.

"Can you walk at all?" said Ben.

"If you help me – yes."

Mark put his arm round Ben's shoulder.
They limped ten paces before Mark fell.

"We're not going to make it like this,"
said Mark. "You'd better leave me. Go and
get help. The next check-point can't be far
away."

Ben bit his lip. He didn't want to leave
Mark – but he had no choice.

"OK. But you take my water. And my
sleeping bag. I'll be as quick as I can ... but
just in case."

Mark nodded. "Sorry for screwing up."

Ben tried to smile. "What are friends
for?"

Ben checked the map and looked at his compass. He guessed it was about three miles to the next check-point.

Half an hour later Ben knew he was lost. He should have found the check-point by now. His chest was burning and his legs felt like rubber. He stared at the sky. He had about three hours until sun-set. Then it would get cold. All Ben had was his running kit and a sweat-shirt. He'd given his sleeping bag to Mark. This was bad. He thought of Belle waiting at home.

Then Ben remembered the mirror.

"I can use it to signal for help!"

He got the tiny mirror out of his back-
pack.

"I hope this works," he said.

The sun flashed on the glass. Over and
over he sent the same message: SOS. I need
help!

For a very long time, there was nothing. Suddenly, he saw a flash of light in the distance. Then another. And another. And then some runners came from behind a dune. Help had come. At last!

The ambulance carrying Mark bounced across the desert. Ben watched until it was out of sight. They had been near a check-point after all.

It was weird for Ben going back to the tent without Mark. One of the soldiers hadn't made it to the finish either. Another victim of the cruel sun.

No one joked now. Everyone had a private battle to fight.

"This is for Belle," said Ben to himself. "And for Mark."

The next day Ben staggered out of his sleeping bag. For mile after mile, he forced his tired body to carry on. His mind was numb.

Suddenly Ben realised that there were people all around him – they were cheering! The finish line was just metres in front of him.

He fell to his knees as he passed the finishing post. Kind hands helped him up.

"I've done it!" he gasped. "I've done it!"

Two days later he was on his way home.

"Man, that was extreme," said Mark softly. "If I hadn't been so stupid, you'd have finished the race in good time."

Ben shrugged his shoulders. "I finished – that means we still get some money for Belle's hospice. That's what matters."

"Yeah, but I didn't finish." Mark frowned. "But I will. I won't let you and Belle down

again. I'm going to come back next year –
and next time I'll finish the race. I promise
you that, bro."

"Better start training," said Ben, smiling.

"Yeah, OK. But I wouldn't mind a week
off first," said Mark. "And an ice cream."

"You got it, bro," laughed Ben. "You got
it!"

Web

by
Alison Prince

Max helps Tim do his home-work. Tim thinks he's a good friend. But Max starts asking for money. Tim can't pay. Max has trapped him like a fly in a web. How can he get out?

You can order *Web* from our website at
www.barringtonstoke.co.uk

Cliff Edge

by
Jane A. C. West

Can Danny make the climb of his life to save his friend?
No ropes, no help – no hope?

You can order *Cliff Edge* from our website at
www.barringtonstoke.co.uk

Snow Dogs

by
Jane A. C. West

Zeb wants to win the dog sled race.
But will he die before he
gets to the end?

You can order *Snow Dogs* from our website at
www.barringtonstoke.co.uk

Sink the Tirpitz

by
Jim Eldridge

The *Tirpitz* is Germany's best war ship.
Can Bob and the crew of his mini
submarine help sink it?
Or will they be blown up themselves?